One Foot
Two Feet

An EXCEPTIONal Counting Book

G. P. Putnam's Sons · An Imprint of Penguin Group (USA) Inc.

One Foot
Two Feet

An EXCEPTIONal Counting Book

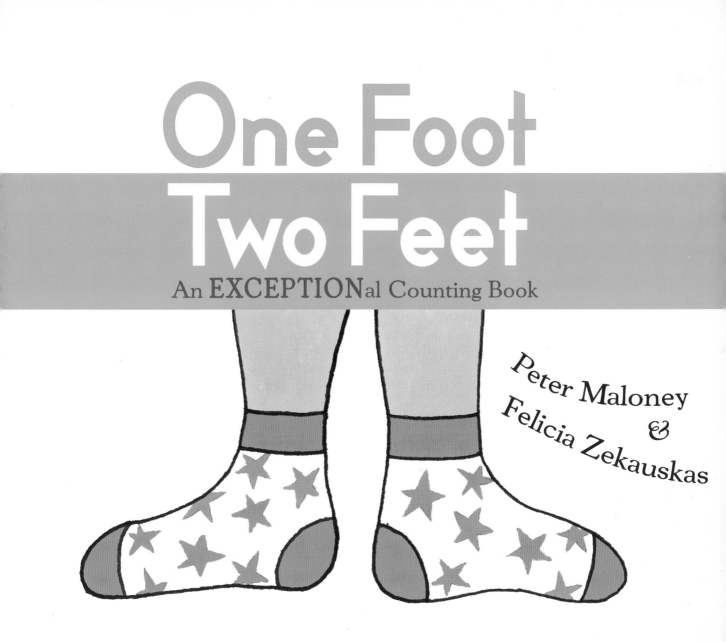

Peter Maloney
&
Felicia Zekauskas

G. P. Putnam's Sons · An Imprint of Penguin Group (USA) Inc.

G. P. PUTNAM'S SONS
A division of Penguin Young Readers Group.
Published by The Penguin Group.
Penguin Group (USA) Inc., 375 Hudson Street, New York, NY 10014, U.S.A.
Penguin Group (Canada), 90 Eglinton Avenue East, Suite 700, Toronto, Ontario M4P 2Y3, Canada
(a division of Pearson Penguin Canada Inc.).
Penguin Books Ltd, 80 Strand, London WC2R 0RL, England.
Penguin Ireland, 25 St. Stephen's Green, Dublin 2, Ireland
(a division of Penguin Books Ltd.).
Penguin Group (Australia), 250 Camberwell Road, Camberwell, Victoria 3124, Australia
(a division of Pearson Australia Group Pty Ltd).
Penguin Books India Pvt Ltd, 11 Community Centre, Panchsheel Park, New Delhi - 110 017, India.
Penguin Group (NZ), 67 Apollo Drive, Rosedale, North Shore 0632, New Zealand
(a division of Pearson New Zealand Ltd).
Penguin Books (South Africa) (Pty) Ltd, 24 Sturdee Avenue, Rosebank, Johannesburg 2196, South Africa.
Penguin Books Ltd, Registered Offices: 80 Strand, London WC2R 0RL, England.

Published simultaneously in Canada. Manufactured in China by South China Printing Co. Ltd.

Design by Marikka Tamura. Text set in CooperOldStyle.
The art was done in acrylic and ink.
Library of Congress Cataloging-in-Publication Data
Maloney, Peter, 1955 Nov. 7–
One foot two feet : an exceptional counting book / Peter Maloney & Felicia Zekauskas.   p. cm.
1. Early childhood education—Activity programs. 2. Mathematics—Study and teaching (Early childhood).
3. Reading (Early childhood)—Language experience approach. I. Zekauskas, Felicia. II. Title.
LB1139.35.A37M35715 2011   372.72—dc22   2010028172
ISBN 978-0-399-25446-8
Special Markets ISBN 978-0-399-25579-3 Not for Resale
3 5 7 9 10 8 6 4

This Imagination Library edition is published by Penguin Group (USA), a Pearson
company, exclusively for Dolly Parton's Imagination Library, a not-for-profit
program designed to inspire a love of reading and learning, sponsored in part by The
Dollywood Foundation. Penguin's trade editions of this work are available wherever
books are sold.

For our two sons,
Christian and Ian

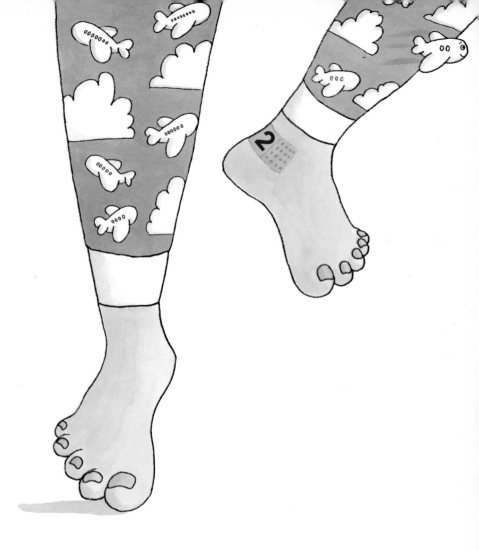

Two Feet

One Mouse

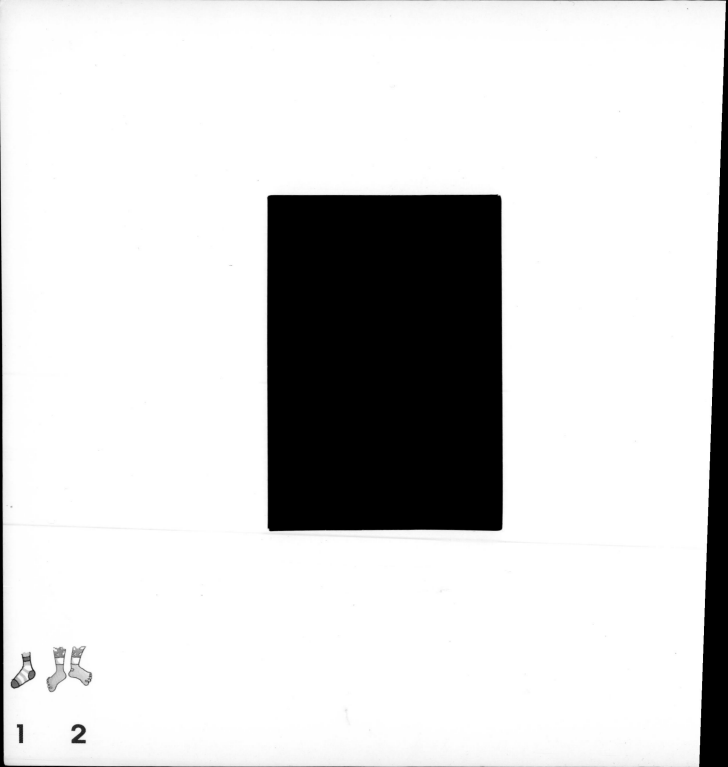

1 2

Three Mice

Four Geese

Four Geese

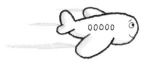

Five Snowmen

One Die

1   2   3   4   5

Six Dice

One Ox

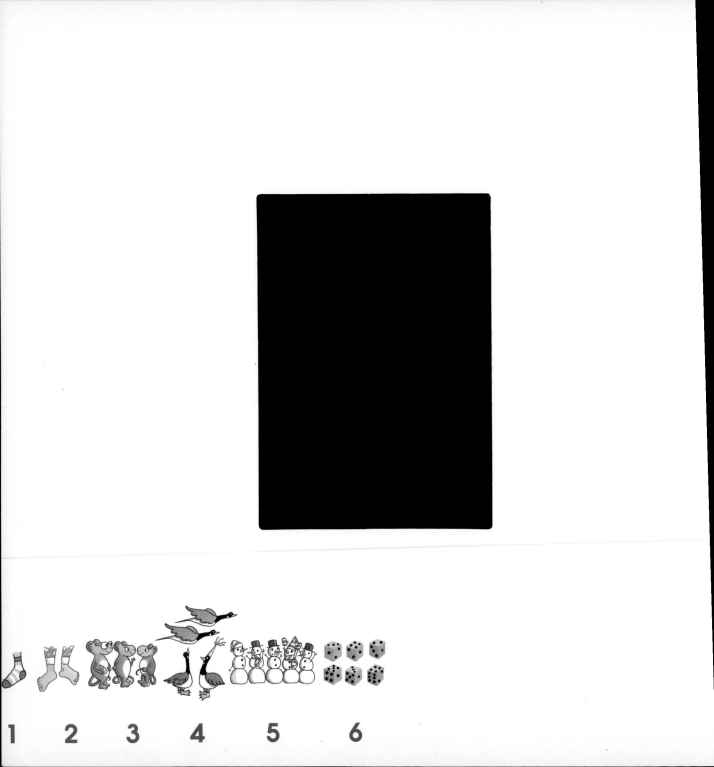

1 2 3 4 5 6

Seven Oxen

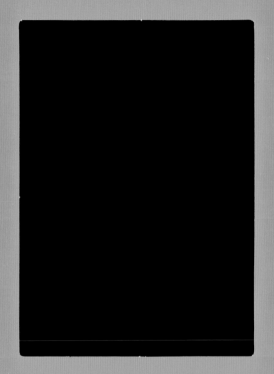

One Octopus

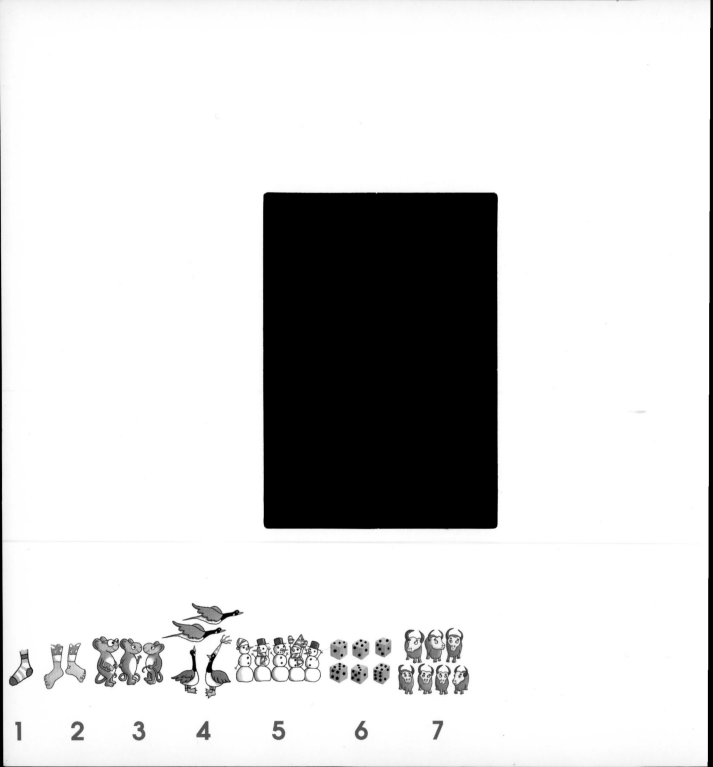

1   2   3   4   5   6   7

Eight Octopi

Nine Teeth

Ten People

A Billion Children

One   Two   Three   Four   Five

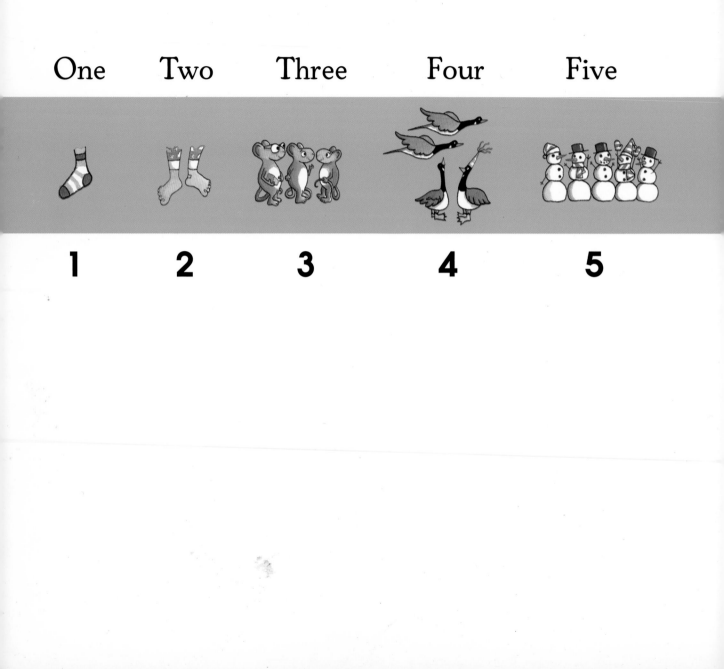

1   2   3   4   5

Six	Seven	Eight	Nine	Ten

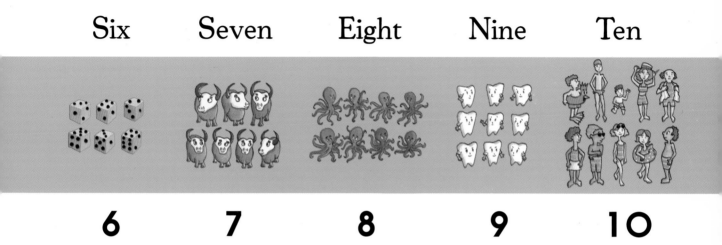

6	7	8	9	10